Man and the Land

150 Years
of
Dorset Farming
1846-1996

J.H. Bettey

Illustration captions by
April Corner and Jo Draper
1996

Dorset Natural History & Archaeological Society

Frontispiece: A champion Dorset Horn ram goes reluctantly into the river to be washed at Coker's Frome, near Dorchester about 1937. Dorset County Museum Collection.

Published by the Dorset Natural History and Archaeological Society, Dorset County Museum, Dorchester DT1 1XA

© DNHAS & J.H. Bettey 1996

Printed by The Friary Press, Dorchester, Dorset

ISBN 0 900341 49 1 : a full CIP record for this book is available.

The Dorset County Museum is grateful to everyone who brought in photographs for the exhibition
Man and the Land – 150 years of Dorset Farming. Some of them have been used for this book.

The publication of this book was made possible by a grant from the Mansel-Pleydell Trust

Herbert Mills leading the bull at Lower Farm, Kington Magna, about 1910. Mr Mills wears a dress-like smock which was worn for milking. Gift of John and Lorna Perrin.

Dorset has always been heavily dependent upon agriculture, and until recent years most people living in the county have been directly or indirectly engaged in farming or one of the associated trades. The county has no natural resources such as coal or iron, and had few major industries, apart from stone-quarrying and clay extraction, so farming has been of crucial importance in the economy of the county, and for several centuries Dorset farming has been distinguished by several major characteristics. The remarkably varied geology of the county underlies three markedly different agricultural regions, and the clay vales of the north and west, the chalk downlands of the central area and the acid soils of the heathland in the south east have traditionally supported quite distinct kinds of farming: milk production and cattle-raising in the vales, sheep and corn husbandry on the downs and in the chalkland valleys, with rough grazing for sheep and cattle, and small-scale arable cultivation on the heaths. Another distinguishing feature has been the dominance of a few great estates and large landowners over many parts of the county, so that society has been clearly divided into three classes; the landowners, the tenant farmers and the large number of agricultural labourers. Traditionally the farms in Dorset were held by copyhold tenure, that is for three named lives 'according to the custom of the manor'. Manorial customs varied from place to place, but most included the obligation on the tenant to pay a 'heriot' or death duty, and specified other requirements on both tenant and landlord. Rents were generally low and the landlord's income was mainly derived from the 'fines' or payments made when a tenant died and a new name was added to the copyhold. These ancient tenures were gradually replaced by leases for a term of years, although copyhold was not finally abolished until 1926.

Sheep shearing at Chilcombe Farm in the later 19th century. The farmer Mr F.F. Samways and his son Frederick on the right. Many of the shearers were itinerant workers, travelling the farms to do the shearing. Gift of Mrs N. Greenings and Mr E. Samways.

Throughout much of the eighteenth and nineteenth centuries Dorset was notorious for the low wages paid to the farm workers and for the long hours of work and poor housing which they had to endure. Another characteristic feature of the county was that until the coming of the railways, the numerous small market towns played a vital role in the lives of the scattered and largely self-sufficient farming communities. The major impression left upon the travellers through the county was of the vast areas of unenclosed downland and heath, and the very large sheep flocks which fed by day on the downs and were folded by night on the arable land. Early in the eighteenth century Daniel Defoe had been impressed by the large sheep flocks which he saw in Dorset during his *Tour through England*, and by the use of the sheep to enrich the arable land. In Dorchester he was told, no doubt with some exaggeration, that 600,000 sheep were fed on the downs in the surrounding region, and although he doubted the figure, he added 'when I viewed the country round, I confess I could not but incline to believe it'. In his *Survey of Dorset Agriculture* published in 1793, John Claridge wrote that

> The most striking feature of the County is the open and uninclosed parts, covered by numerous flocks of sheep, scattered over the Downs ...

It was to provide early grass and abundant hay for the sheep flocks that the water meadows, which were such a remarkable feature of Dorset agriculture, had been developed and created throughout the chalkland valleys from the early seventeenth century, and had become such a vital feature of farming practice.

Every aspect of farming in Dorset, as elsewhere in England, has seen dramatic and revolutionary changes during the past 150 years, with enormous alterations in the landscape, vast increases in productivity, the introduction of machinery, electricity, new breeds of livestock, new crops, improved varieties, artificial fertilisers, pesticides, fungicides, a huge decline in the labour force and a host of other developments. The following account describes the major features of Dorset agriculture and the remarkable innovations which have affected farming and rural society in the county during the nineteenth and twentieth centuries.

The Napoleonic War Period

Since the Napoleonic Wars Dorset farming has experienced a series of peaks and troughs; periods of high prosperity have been followed by times of acute depression, and these fluctuating fortunes have greatly affected the whole population of the county. The sharp rise in population during the eighteenth century, followed by the long struggle against Napoleonic France which lasted from 1793 until the Battle of Waterloo and the Treaty of Vienna in 1815, brought with it a greatly increased demand for home produced foodstuffs. Prices rose steeply and farmers' profits increased accordingly, while market towns flourished as did the trades associated with farming. Wheat which had sold for 43s 0d per imperial quarter (8 bushels) in 1793 was making 109s 9d by 1815 and had even sold for 126s 6d in 1812. Barley had more than doubled in price from 30s 0d per imperial quarter in 1793 to 67s 0d per quarter by 1812. The prices of beef and mutton likewise doubled over the war years from about 3s 6d a stone in 1793 to 6s 6d a stone by 1815. The consequence of these greatly inflated prices was a concerted drive for improved agricultural productivity. Farmers rushed to benefit from the massively increased profits to be made from the sale of their produce, investing heavily in new leases, equipment and stock, without regard to the inevitable collapse of prices which would come with the ending of the war. Since Dorset is divided into three very distinct farming regions, it is impossible to generalise about the farming of the county as a whole, but everywhere the effect of inflated wartime prices and the opportunities for large profits brought new developments in farming. In the clay vales where small dairy farms predominated, changes came slowly, and the peculiar Dorset system whereby farmers hired out their cows to dairymen still continued. This practice whereby the farmer supplied the cows and all the food required at the rate of 2½-3 acres per cow, partly for summer grazing and partly for hay in the winter, in return for an agreed rent per cow, was continued in Dorset throughout the nineteenth century. The farmer was freed from the daily chores of the dairy while the dairyman, whose rent frequently included the 'Dairy House', supported his family from the sale of butter, cheese and pigs. Dorset butter in particular was held in high regard and commanded a premium in the London markets. Even so the increased prices for butter and cheese led to some improvements including drainage of pastures, the introduction of clovers, sainfoin, ryegrass, lucerne, turnips and other fodder crops, and greater attention to the milk-producing capacity of breeding stock. In parts of west Dorset, notably at Broadwindsor, Netherbury, Beaminster, Symondsbury, Loders, Bradpole and Powerstock, the rich clayland soils also grew hemp and flax for the production of rope, twine and sailcloth which were greatly in demand during wartime. This industry was to remain important and during the early nineteenth century continued to use large quantities of home-grown flax as well as imported supplies. Abbotsbury, Bridport, Beaminster and other places in the district also grew potatoes on a large scale.

It was, however, on the chalklands that the most striking changes occurred under the impetus of the high corn prices, since this was the region where the production of wheat and barley was the principal aim of farmers. Before the advent of artificial fertilisers the regular folding of the sheep flocks on the arable land was an essential feature of corn production on the thin chalkland soils, and it was for this purpose that the large sheep flocks were maintained. In 1793 John Claridge in his *Survey of Dorset Agriculture* gave a careful account of the system of the sheep fold

> The sheep are constantly attended by a shepherd the whole day ... The wether sheep are constantly folded all the year round, running over the ewe leas or downs by day, and are penned on the tillage by night. They are penned late in the evening in the winter, and not later than six o'clock in the summer.

The Dorset Horn sheep were admirably suited to folding, and this use of the sheep flocks to maintain the productivity of the cornlands was the sheet anchor of Dorset chalkland farming, overcoming the lack of fertility in the soil while profiting from its free-draining characteristics which were described as 'a natural drain, which never chokes, and which charges no interest for capital'. It was in order to keep ever larger sheep flocks and thus grow more wheat and barley that the water meadows had been constructed to supply early grass for ewes and lambs and to produce abundant crops of hay for winter feed. No other county had such a large proportion of water meadows and nowhere were they more carefully managed. By the end of the Napoleonic Wars it was estimated that more than 6,000 acres of water meadows were in use along the chalkland streams of Dorset. It was a Dorset farmer, George Boswell of Puddletown, who wrote the best-known account of the creation and working of water-meadows in his *Treatise on Water Meadows* published in 1779. This was dedicated to two Dorset landowners, the Earl of Ilchester of Melbury and to James Frampton of Moreton, and provided a full account of the methods and benefits of watering meadows.

Enclosures

The changes in chalkland farming brought about by the wartime conditions and prices included the enclosure by Act of Parliament of many of the former open fields in which the tenants' strips of arable land had been intermingled one with another and their replacement by enclosed compact farms. At the same time there was a considerable increase in the size of farms, an extension of arable cultivation on the slopes of the downland, an increased use and development of water meadows and new fodder crops to provide increased feed for the ever larger sheep flocks necessary to maintain increased corn production. Forty-four per cent of all Dorset enclosures by Act of Parliament took place during the period 1793-1815. By the end of the war in 1815 a great deal of the open downland had been enclosed and brought under cultivation, and new farms had been built which can still be recognised by their architecture, their large well-built barns and granaries, and by their names, such as Botany Bay, Normandy, Canada, Quatre Bras, or the numerous New Down and New Barn Farms. The drive for greater productivity and profit also led to the introduction of new iron ploughs, harrows, drills and other implements. The increase in the size of farms resulted in the disappearance of the formerly numerous small-holders, a fact greatly lamented by the Dorset poet, William Barnes

> Then ten good deäries [dairies] wer a-ved
> Along that water's winden bed,
> An' in the length o'hills an' wood
> A half a score farm-housen stood:
> But now, - count all o'm how you would,
> So many less do hold the land, -
> You'd vind but vive that still do stand,
> A'comen down vrom gramfer's.

That Barnes was not exaggerating the disappearance of the Dorset small-holder is evident from the example of Bere Regis. In 1776 there were 46 tenant farmers of whom 26 farmed less than 30 acres each. Much of the arable land consisted of intermingled strips in the open felds, but by 1796 many of the smaller tenements had been swallowed up by the larger farmers who were farming in a much more profit-conscious manner. Long before the formal end of the open fields of Bere Regis by a Parliamentary Enclosure Act of 1846, the 26 smaller holdings had been swallowed up by the 20 larger farms. Even more dramatic was the situation at Durweston where 30 small farms in the eighteenth century were 'engrossed' or gradually amalgamated to form 2 large farms by the early nineteenth century. Even on the heavier lands the same influences were at work, and at Trent, for example, the number of farms declined from 68 in 1740 to 41 in 1783, while by 1839 the number of farms had sunk to 12. Such enclosures transformed the landscape of many parishes. A typical example is Winterborne Monkton which belonged to the Dean and Chapter of Exeter cathedral. A map of 1773 shows the village beneath the great ramparts of Maiden Castle, with meadow land along the stream, three large open fields with tenants' arable land in scattered strips,

and with large areas of surrounding downland where the manorial sheep flock grazed during the day before being folded on the arable lands at night. In 1808 an Act of Parliament was obtained authorising enclosure, and during the following year the whole landscape was changed. The open arable fields were swept away and both arable and downland was enclosed into large rectangular fields divided by thorn hedges, creating the modern landscape, with only the former Roman road running from Dorchester to the Ridgway surviving from the former landscape. The cost of such enclosures was beyond the scope of many smaller tenants and so the number of farms declined rapidly leaving fewer much larger farms in their place. There is no doubt that enclosure brought improved productivity and profits, and that greatly increased rents could be charged by landlords for the larger farms. Average rents per acre in Dorset rose from about 12s 0d in the eighteenth century to almost 30s 0d by 1815. Moreover, many farms were let on ten, twelve or fourteen year leases which specified the crop rotations, cultivations and general husbandry which was to be employed on the farm.

The Heath

Change came more slowly and less dramatically to the poorly-drained, acid soils of the heathlands, but even here the high prices of corn and meat during the Napoleonic Wars led to considerable reclamation and conversion to arable, especially around the edges of the heath, with enclosure, drainage, turf-burning and the application of large quantities of chalk or lime to improve the soil quality. A few years earlier, in 1771, the well-known agricultural observer, Arthur Young, had been dismayed by the sight of the heath, unused and still in its natural state, and ignoring all the practical difficulties had written of the

> Vast tracts of waste land that call aloud for improvements ... What fortunes are here to be made by spirited improvers!

Young's hasty and over-optimistic comment was clearly ill-judged, but some improvements were made, drainage ditches were dug, arable land was extended and grassland was improved for sheep, dairy cows and beef cattle. Farms on the heath, however, remained small, and many farmers continued to have some secondary employment such as clay mining, quarrying, turf-cutting, coppice-work, employment in Poole or Wareham, or at various crafts and trades.

The Labourers

In the comfortable security of rising prices many Dorset farmers and their landlords enjoyed great prosperity during the wartime years, commanding wealth which is still evident from the fine houses and farmsteads which they built and from their lavish monuments in the parish churches. Unfortunately the labourers did not share in this good fortune, and Dorset became a by-word for the low wages, poor

housing and bad conditions of farm workers. The end of the war in 1815 brought a sharp decline in corn prices and, for example, wheat fell from 120s per quarter in 1815 to 65s per quarter in 1820, and the prices of barley, beef, mutton and cheese fell by more than 50 per cent. Many farmers who had borrowed heavily to support improvements in the expectation of continuing high prices found themselves in great difficulties and there were numerous bankruptcies. At the same time the plight of the labourers became even worse and was to remain a reproach to the county throughout much of the first half of the nineteenth century. Even during the wartime period of high prices and farming prosperity, the labourers and their families were poorly paid, ill-housed and inadequately fed. In 1797 Sir Frederick Morton Eden published his *State of the Poor* which was based on careful research in

A crowd watching labourers being evicted from their cottages at Milborne St Andrew in April 1874. The labourers had demanded 14 shillings a week - they were being paid 12 shillings. When the farmers refused, the labourers went on strike and were then evicted. Dorset County Museum Collection.

many parts of England. In Dorset Eden visited the Blandford Forum district and found that the labourers were suffering because of

> the high price of provisions, the smallness of wages, and the consolidation of farms, and the consequent depopulation of villages, which obliges small farmers to turn labourers or servants.

One labourer who was interviewed by Eden earned 6s 0d a week in winter and 7s 0d a week in summer. His wife had recently died, and he and his four children lived almost entirely on bread, cheese and potatoes. 'Bullock's cheek is generally bought every week to make broth. Treacle is used to sweeten tea instead of sugar. Very little milk or beer is used'. This family was regarded by Eden as typical and not especially deprived. During the early decades of the nineteenth century the condition of the Dorset labourer deteriorated even further. Following the end of the war in 1815 and the collapse in the price of farm produce, labourers' wages fell while unemployment and poverty increased greatly, forcing many to apply for poor relief, so that the next few years were a period of unparalleled poverty, degradation and misery in the county. During the war wages for farm labourers had reached as high as 12s 0d a week in 1814, but by 1817 they had fallen back to 7s 0d a week and were to remain at that level for the next twenty-five years. Many would have echoed William Cobbett's indignant protest made in *Rural Rides* during 1826 in the Avon valley near Salisbury

> This is, I verily believe it, the worst used labouring people upon the face of the earth. Dogs and hogs and horses are treated with more civility; and as to food and lodging, how gladly would the labourers change with them!

The population of the county continued to rise, from 114,000 in 1801 to 184,000 in 1851, making the

Participants in a late 19th century sheep-shearing contest, many looking lile Gabriel Oak, the shepherd of Hardy's novel Far from the Madding Crowd. *Gift of Mrs G.L. Davies & Mrs A. Hirst.*

problems of poverty and unemployment even worse.

The typical trend of population revealed in the Census Returns in most of the rural parishes of Dorset during the nineteenth century was a steady increase between 1801 and 1851 or 1861, and thereafter a sharp fall as the demand for farm labourers declined and as families moved to the industrial towns or took advantage of the opportunities for emigration. The result was that many parishes had fewer inhabitants in 1901 than they had in 1801. The following examples provide the figures for the population of a selection of towns and villages across the county.

Population Trends in Some Dorset Towns & Villages 1801-1851

	1801	1851	1901
Affpuddle	344	488	358
Alton Pancras	184	270	183
Askerswell	170	224	179
Beaminster	2140	2832	1702
Bere Regis	936	1242	1236
Bradford Abbas	480	621	391
Broadwindsor	1094	1516	994
Burton Bradstock	654	1181	715
Cerne Abbas	847	1343	643
Chideock	578	884	551
Corfe Castle	1344	1966	1440
Corscombe	515	772	543
Cranborne	1801	2737	2464
Durweston	332	406	396
Evershot	497	606	353
Fontmell Magna	628	832	566
Gussage All Saints	301	477	347
Halstock	397	572	357
Hazelbury Bryan	454	709	541
Hilton	462	761	502
Lulworth East	364	450	294
Lulworth West	312	401	358
Milborne St Andrew	257	485	334
Moreton	256	227	356
Okeford Fitzpaine	341	368	221
Piddletrenthide	449	800	587
Pimperne	316	517	375
Powerstock	802	1044	631
Shaftesbury	3047	3992	3403
Spetisbury	336	660	457
Stourpaine	380	621	493
Sturminster Newton	1406	1916	1877
Toller Porcorum	340	527	337
Whitchurch Canonicorum	932	1532	868
Wimborne St Giles	350	495	425
Winfrith Newburgh	569	1101	820
Winterborne Stickland	306	407	365
Winterborne Whitchurch	430	595	357
Winterborne Zelston	233	224	122
Wool	383	545	497
Wootton Fitzpaine	355	361	154
Worth Matravers	217	350	276

'Captain Swing' Riots and the Tolpuddle Martyrs

It was the combination of low wages, poor conditions and unemployment, together with the bad winters and poor harvests of 1829 and 1830 that finally led to the great explosion of anger and frustration known as the 'Captain Swing' riots of November 1830. These riots with their associated rick-burning and machine breaking swept through the whole of southern England, supposedly led by the fictitious 'Captain Swing'. There were two main areas of rioting in Dorset, the central corn-growing chalklands between Dorchester and Wimborne, and the traditionally lawless and unruly region of Cranborne Chase. Both areas were characterised by vast estates and very large farms. The smaller, family-run farms in the dairying pastoral area of west Dorset were not affected. Labourers around Bere Regis assembled to demand wages of 10s 0d per week, and the riots spread to the areas around Wareham and Puddletown where ricks were burnt and threshing machines smashed. Large numbers of labourers assembled at Blandford and Shaftesbury, and at Sixpenny Handley a magistrate reported that 'had we committed for participating in and aiding the burning of machinery, we might have committed two-thirds of the labouring population of the district'. Threatening letters were received by a number of landowners. One to Edward Castleman, whose estates were in the Wimborne area, declared

> Mr Castleman, Sir,
> Sunday night your House shall come down to the Ground for you are an inhuman monster and we will dash out your brains -Banks and your sett aught to be sent to Hell. The Hanley Torches have not forgot you.

In all there were more than forty separate riots in the county. Meanwhile, there was frenzied activity by the county magistrates. Great numbers of special constables were sworn in, the yeomanry and the coastguards were brought in to help quell the mobs, and vigorous arrangements were made by landowners to defend their property. Some concessions were made. Farmers in the Puddletown area agreed to raise wages to 10s 0d a week; in the Gillingham area wages were increased to 9s 0d. At the same time large numbers of men were arrested for taking part in unlawful assemblies and were imprisoned. Not all were captured of course. During a rising at Winfrith, James Frampton of Moreton, one of the most active and unpopular of the magistrates, grabbed one man from the mob, but the man slipped out of his smock and escaped leaving it behind. By early December 1830 more troops arrived, and the riots died out.

In January 1831, sixty-two prisoners were tried by a Special Commission at Dorchester, of whom thirteen were sentenced to transportation for life for their part in the attempt to gain a living wage. A petition was presented to the king to get these sentences reduced, but as Mary Frampton, sister of James Frampton, wrote in her journal, 'Fortunately ... as they were already on board the transports and the wind fair, the petition would be too late. Care was taken at the deportation of these men ... to send them to those parts of New Zealand and New Holland where their agricultural knowledge and labour might be useful. Thus very probably at a future time rendering our disturbances here a blessing to our Antipodes'. The few temporary

improvements in wages secured in 1830 were quickly lost and the Dorset farm workers were soon in as desperate a condition as before. This gave rise to the famous attempt to found the Friendly Society of Agricultural Labourers at Tolpuddle in 1833. Some forty labourers joined this society and it was hoped that it would be the forerunner of others in Dorset. But the labourers reckoned without the determination of the government and the local magistrates, with memories of the 'Captain Swing' riots of 1830 still fresh. In particular they had to contend with the magistrate chiefly concerned with the Tolpuddle area, James Frampton, who was passionately concerned with maintaining law and order and with stamping out anything that might lead to civil disobedience and unrest. He reacted very harshly and the Tolpuddle Martyrs were tried and transported in 1834. The fate of these unfortunate men whose unwitting breach of the draconian laws of the time led to such disastrous consequences for them and their families meant the end of any attempt to spread agricultural trade unionism in Dorset for more than a generation and their conditions remained harsh. Throughout much of the nineteenth century, wages were low and the proportion of the population dependent upon poor relief continued to be much higher than in the industrial areas of the Midlands and the North. In 1855, for example the average poor rate charge upon householders in the industrial towns was 1s 0d in the pound, while in Dorset it was more than 2s 0d. In the North the poor accounted for 3.5 per cent of the population, while in Dorset the proportion was 5 per cent. By 1898 the average weekly wage of Dorset labourers was 11s 0d per week compared to 16s 0d in the Midlands. Few alternative opportunities for employment were available to Dorset farm labourers whose bargaining position with the large farmers and great landowners remained very weak.

Cottages and Housing Conditions for Labourers

The New Poor Law of 1834, with its system of grim Union workhouses which are still to be seen in many parts of Dorset, failed to eliminate poverty, and the evidence of numerous Parliamentary commissions and Reports throughout the nineteenth century bears witness to the continuing low wages and bad housing of the Dorset farm labourers. For example in 1843 Rachel Hayward, the wife of John Hayward, a farm labourer from Stourpaine gave evidence to Parliamentary commissioners about the crowded conditions and meagre, monotonous diet which she and her family were obliged to endure.

There are eleven of us in our family -myself, my husband, three daughters and six sons. We have two rooms, one down stairs and the other up stairs over it. We all sleep in the bedroom. My husband gets 8s or 7s a week; my two eldest daughters get about 3s 6d a week at buttoning, and three of my boys get 5s a week together; in all about 16s 6d a week. We have 16½ lugs of potato-ground on which we grow potatoes and a few vegetables; for that we pay 7s 7d a year rent.

We pay 1s a week for the cottage, and coal and wood cost us 1s 8d a week at this time of year (December). We get ¾ cwt. of coal a week, I buy besides, every week ¾ lb soap, 1 oz. tea, ½ lb bacon. I reckon we eat a pound of bread each day; that with the potatoes gives us enough. My three boys that are out at work went out at nine years old.

This family was evidently greatly helped by the daughters' employment at button-making, while elsewhere in Dorset some low-paid employment

Sheep at Bovington in the 1930s. Gift of Mr Chutter.

could be obtained in the part-time manufacture of gloves, lace or nets. Some farmers allowed their labourers to have small plots of ground to grow potatoes, which meant that during the summer and autumn when well-paid work was available elsewhere the labourer was unlikely to leave the farm since he would then lose his potato crop. The plight of Dorset farm labourers was brought to national attention during the 1840s by the famous series of letters to *The Times* newspaper by Sidney Godolphin Osborne, the well-connected rector of Durweston, known as S.G.O. from the signature to his letters. Later, Thomas Hardy also published an account of *The Dorset Farm Labourer* (1883).

In 1867 a Parliamentary Commission appointed to enquire into 'The Employment of Children and Young Persons and Women in Agriculture' produced a mass of evidence on working conditions and housing in Dorset. It reported that hours of work were commonly from 6 am to 6 pm, wages were 7 or 8 shillings a week and that boys were employed from the age of 10 and in some places as young as 7 years of age. Labourers' cottages in many villages were described as very bad. One commissioner reported that

the cottages of this county (Dorset) are more ruinous and contain worse accommodation than those of any other county I have visited, except Shropshire.... Such villages as Bere Regis, Fordington, Winfrith, Cranborne or Charminster (in which there is an average of 7 persons to a house) ... are a disgrace to the owners of the land, and contain many cottages unfit for human habitation.... In village after village ... there is nothing like one privy to each cottage. I saw whole rows of cottages with none, and abounding in miseries of all kinds. ... the state of filth in which many parishes are left calls aloud for some active interference.

Annual contracts for farm labourers made at the local hiring fairs remained usual in Dorset throughout the nineteenth century, and in the

absence of major local industries there were few opportunities for Dorset labourers to secure alternative or better-paid employment.

Estate Cottages

Some estate owners did make a valiant effort to improve their cottages and to provide benefits such as potato-ground and fuel allotments, for example, well-built new cottages with good facilities were built by Lord Portman at Pimperne and Durweston, by Henry Charles Sturt on his extensive estate around Crichel, on the Ilchester estates at Melbury and Abbotsbury, the Duke of Bedford's estate at Swyre, on the Brymer property at Puddletown and the Grosvenor estate at Motcombe and numerous others. Some landlords were embarrassed by the condition of the cottages on their estates.

When the philanthropist seventh Earl of Shaftesbury succeeded to the Wimborne St Giles estate in 1851, he found the accounts in chaos, a mass of debts and the farms and cottages in a deplorable situation. In despair he wrote

Alas, I am powerless; I can neither build cottages nor dismiss the farmer from his land without money to fall back upon.

He also deplored the fact that although he had been so outspoken in his condemnation of the bad housing in the industrial towns, and had so strongly stressed the influence of dwellings on the habits and character of labourers, he had inherited a large estate with such appalling housing conditions.

I have passed my life in rating others for allowing rotten houses and immoral, unhealthy dwellings; and now I come into an estate rife with abominations! Why, there are things here to make one's flesh creep; and I have not a farthing to set them right.

By great efforts, including the sale of land and plate, Lord Shaftesbury was able to transform the estate, and by the time of his death in 1885 his agent could report that of 537 cottages on the estate 12 were 'bad', 77 were in 'fair repair' and the rest were 'excellent'. But many landowners, however willing to spend money on improvements to their labourers' cottages, were prevented from doing so by the copyhold tenure or continuing leases granted to their tenant farmers which effectively prevented any improvements until the termination of the lease. In addition, many of the worst cottages were the property of smaller landowners or of tradesmen from local towns who lacked either the incentive or the resources to improve them, while others had been erected by the occupants themselves as squatters on waste ground, roadside verges or heathland.

'High Farming' in the Mid-Nineteenth Century

The slump in farming following the end of the Napoleonic War in 1815 and characterised by much reduced prices for wheat, barley, meat and butter continued during the 1820s. Farmers' difficulties were exacerbated by unseasonable weather and poor harvests in 1817-18, 1821-3 and 1828-9, and by outbreaks of sheep-rot during 1828-30. For landowners this meant further reductions of rent and of expenditure on estate improvements. Gradually, however, prosperity returned during the 1830s and 1840s as the demand for food increased from the rapidly-growing populations of the industrial towns of the Midlands and the North, as prices increased, and as the railways brought a new era both for the sale of produce and for the purchase of supplies. This was to be the beginning of a period of rapid and profound changes in Dorset farming, the period of 'High Farming' with a new scientific approach, high inputs of artificial fertilisers and manufactured feedstuffs, high capital investment in buildings, stock, implements, drainage and motive power, and much higher yields than had previously been obtained. Dorset farmers and landowners shared fully in the mid-Victorian enthusiasm for improvement and experimentation in all branches of agriculture. New and improved breeds of cattle and sheep were introduced, and new methods of butter and cheese making with a much greater emphasis on cleanliness and on the creation of a high quality, standardised product. The new ideas were spread by farmers' clubs which became popular during this period, where farmers could exchange views and learn new ideas. The most influential society, the Bath and West of England Society, was founded as early as 1777 and its *Journal* and experimental farming rapidly became extremely influential. Local

A steam traction engine in the farmyard at Chilcombe, with its chimney lowered and covered with a tarpaulin. Gift of Mrs Nora Greenings and Mr E. Samways.

societies within the county came later but also had a profound effect in publicising the most up-to-date methods and the application of science to agriculture. They also promoted improvements in farming practice by competitions, ploughing matches, prizes for the best crops such as turnips or the best livestock. The Royal Agricultural Society of England was founded in 1838, and this was soon followed by numerous local societies and farmers' clubs, including those at Sturminster Newton, Blandford, Winfrith, Milborne St Andrew, Dorchester, Sherborne, Stalbridge, Wareham, Gillingham, Isle of Purbeck, Lulworth and Shaftesbury. During this mid nineteenth-century period of prosperity and 'high farming' many of the major landowners and tenant farmers were active in promoting new ideas, introducing new methods and investing in improved crops, artificial fertilisers and new breeds of cattle and sheep. On his extensive estates around Bryanston, Lord Portman built improved farmsteads, introduced new implements and improved cultivations, new crop rotations and the regular use of turnips, rape, sainfoin and other fodder crops. From his home at Rushmore near Tollard Royal, Lord Rivers provided new and improved farmsteads and cattle housing on his Cranborne Chase estates, while Henry Charles Sturt of Crichel and John James Farquharson of Langton were foremost in using steam power for threshing and other farm-yard tasks. Other influential landowners and farmers included Sir Edward Hambro at Milton Abbas, and the Tory family of Turnworth whose widespread farms in central Dorset were noted for the high quality of their sheep flocks, their arable crops and for their dairy herd. A notable exponent of scientific farming methods was Professor James Buckman who had been professor of geology and botany at the Cirencester Agricultural college and who took over a large farm at Bradford Abbas in 1863 and conducted it according to the latest ideas. He wrote regularly in farming journals, and also lectured to many farmers' clubs being particularly enthusiastic in recommending the use of artificial fertilisers and root crops especially swedes. He himself was awarded a trophy in 1865 for the best crop of swedes,

achieving 4½ tons per acre through the use of artificial fertilisers.

On the Digby estates around Sherborne, the Ilchester estates at Melbury, Evershot and Abbotsbury and the Duke of Bedford's estate at Kingston Russell very large sums were spent on land drainage and improvements to pasture. The well-run farms on these estates were intended to provide examples of the best practice and a pattern to be followed by other farmers in the district. The best-known of all the Dorset 'example farms' were those established by the Revd. Anthony Huxtable at Sutton Waldron where he was the rector from 1834 to 1871. In order to demonstrate the newest scientific methods and to show what could be achieved by the application of science to agriculture, Huxtable took over two local farms, reconstructed the buildings, installed steam engines and elaborate systems for delivering liquid manure to the fields. He established a national reputation for his farming experiments, publishing his work through the *Journal* of the Royal Agricultural Society of which he became a prominent member. Huxtable's farming methods included deep draining with heavy applications of lime and manure. He also provided housing for his cattle and sheep, and pioneered the use of steam power for threshing, grinding, chaffcutting and the pumping of liquid manure. His experiments with both arable crops and livestock attracted great attention and publicity, not by any means all of it favourable, and many were quick to point out that Huxtable was a wealthy man who could afford the large capital which his methods required. His remarkable career, however, remains an excellent example of the interest and enthusiasm which was devoted to agriculture and agricultural improvement in the mid-nineteenth century. The advances which had been made in providing new kinds of implements, equipment and the motive power of steam engines for farmers were spectacularly demonstrated at the agricultural sections of the Great Exhibition of 1851. By then it was clear that the disasters predicted for farming by the repeal of the protective Corn Laws in 1846 had not materialised in spite of all the fears that had been expressed and the vocal, though unsuccessful, campaign against repeal mounted by farmers in Dorset and throughout the country.

Railways and Steam Power

In Dorset a great impetus to improved farming was provided by the arrival of the railways which reached Dorchester in 1847, Yetminster, Evershot, Maiden Newton, Bridport and Weymouth in 1857 and Sherborne in 1860. Thereafter, within a few years most parts of the county had reasonable access to a railway station. The effects on farming were tremendous. The railways revolutionised the dairy industry. For the first time liquid milk could be carried quickly and efficiently to the towns; new feed stuffs could be brought cheaply and conveniently to supplement the feed for sheep and cattle, for example, Thorley's cattle cake, compounded of grain and vegetable oils, became available during the 1850s. For arable farmers the railways brought new implements, drainage pipes, artificial manures, guano, bone meal, new varieties and strains of seeds, and also provided a totally new way of marketing the produce of the land, completely by-passing local markets and the often lower local prices. For the more adventurous young people in Dorset, the railways offered an opportunity to escape from poorly-paid farm labouring and to seek better rewarded work in the industrial towns or in the colonies. The depopulation of so many Dorset villages during the second half of the nineteenth century started first with girls leaving to work as domestic servants or shop assistants in the growing resorts of Bournemouth and Weymouth, or in the rapidly-expanding towns further afield. As Barbara Kerr described in her book *Bound to the Soil* (1968), during the 1870s

> in every Dorset village eager girls with small corded trunks awaited the carrier's cart to take them on the first stage of their townward journey.

They were soon followed by young men who left the land to seek work in the factory towns of the Midlands and North of England or seized the opportunities of assisted passages to seek better

conditions and a new life in the colonies. The results of their departure can be seen in the figures of population decline shown on page 11. Rural depopulation continued in Dorset during the early twentieth century, and between 1871 and 1911 the labour force employed on farms in the county fell by 31%.

The mid-nineteenth century also saw the introduction of new and greatly improved breeds of cattle and sheep, and a much more selective approach to breeding and animal husbandry. The traditional flocks of Dorset Horn sheep were replaced over many parts of the chalk downlands by South Downs, Hampshire Downs and Dorset Downs which provided a more acceptable and faster maturing carcass, although the Dorset Horn remained supreme for the production of early lambs. The mixed herds of unimproved Longhorn beef and dairy cows vanished from the more progressive farms, to be replaced by herds of Devon or Hereford beef cattle and by milking herds of Channel Islands, Ayrshire or Dairy Shorthorns. The Shorthorns were introduced about 1870 and rapidly became by far the most popular breed. At the same time the attack on the remaining open, unimproved downland continued, and all over the chalklands several thousand acres were each year enclosed and newly brought into cultivation, a process which was to be greatly speeded by the introduction of steam ploughing during the 1860s. In 1866, for example, one of the newly-developed steam ploughing systems was used to break up several hundred acres of former open downland at Alton Pancras. Notwithstanding the speed and efficiency with which the steam plough could convert the downland to arable, the capital cost of the equipment, which was as much as £1,600 for a ploughing set, put it beyond the reach of individual farmers, but this difficulty was overcome by contractors. The first attempts at steam ploughing by contract were made by Mr Henry Taylor and Mr John Galpin of Dorchester but these failed to overcome the Dorset farmers' suspicions of the new system. In 1870, however, Francis Eddison established his Steam Ploughing Works at Dorchester from where his numerous sets of steam ploughs were hired to bring

Harvest at Waterson about 1900, with oxen pulling the cart. By this date oxen were uncommon in Dorset.

Fifty years later the Hinton family haymaking at Waterson in 1946. Gift of Mr and Mrs Woodsford.

many thousands of acres of virgin downland across the county into cultivation during the next two decades. Eddison adopted the system developed by John Fowler of Leeds, which used a pair of steam engines, one on each headland, to pull the plough to and fro between them across the field, a method which proved to be the most efficient and popular and which dominated the market until it was superseded by the tractor during the twentieth century. The path for Eddison's enterprise had been prepared by John Fowler's representative, Thomas Richardson, who addressed the Dorchester Farmers' Club in January 1870 and spoke with missionary fervour of the advantages of steam cultivation. Richardson's speech was reported in detail by the *Dorset County Chronicle*. He described steam power as 'the great abridger of time and labour' ensuring that 'a brighter morn is now dawning upon the farmers' prospects'. He claimed that the steam plough would 'cultivate more deeply, cheaply and rapidly, leaving a mellower and warmer soil'; it would increase yields, greatly reduce toil and improve the lot of the labourer, and represented 'a glorious triumph of human genius over soulless matter', increasing the wealth of the nation and the well-being of all classes of society.

During the 1870s Eddison's steam ploughing works prospered, and eventually he had twelve double-engined plough sets which were hired for work all over the county. Demand was greatly reduced during the agricultural depression of the 1880s, however, and by the time of his death in 1888 Eddison had diverted part of his enterprise to steam rollers and road-making equipment.

The 'Golden Age' of Dorset Farming

The effect of 'high farming' on the agriculture, the landscape and the economy of Dorset was dramatic. All over the county farmers sought the most profitable methods and took immense pride in their livestock, husbandry, crops and cultivations. Weeds were banished, arable and pasture was drained, improved and fertilised as never before, and livestock reached a standard which would have amazed earlier generations of farmers. There are several accounts of Dorset farming during this period of prosperity and experimentation. In February 1850 Sir James Caird, the noted agricultural writer, visited Dorset on his tour through England and wrote a detailed account of the farming practices in the county. He described the butter-producing farms of west Dorset and the contrast between the small fields in the clay vales and the large farms of the chalklands and the great expanses of downland with few hedges and with the large flocks of sheep kept for folding on the arable land. In 1850 the cultivation of swedes, clover, rape and vetches as spring feed for the sheep flocks was well-established on the chalklands, as was the use of artificial manures, bone-meal, guano and superphosphate. He found that the water meadows were carefully managed 'and furnish very useful early food for ewes and lambs, and hay for them in the winter'. Already the Southdown breed had replaced the old Dorset breed of sheep through much of central Dorset. Considerably more detail was provided by L.H. Ruegg, the editor of a Dorset newspaper, who wrote a prize essay for the Royal Agricultural Society in 1854 on *The Farming of Dorsetshire*. Ruegg described many of the advances which were taking place and the high standard of farming which was becoming general throughout the county, and wrote that 'From Woodyates to six miles beyond Dorchester (nearly the entire length of the chalk district) there is no better farming in the kingdom'.

After describing at length and with numerous examples the farming in the three regions of the county, Ruegg summarised the improvements which had been made during the previous forty years. These included greatly improved crop rotations and the introduction of turnips, sainfoin, clover, rape and other fodder crops.

Ruegg gave details of the widespread use of new and improved implements, and of steam power by the more progressive farmers both for barn work and for threshing. Much better farm buildings had been erected on the farms belonging to many of the great estates and the new enclosures had produced great improvements in farming practice. Parliamentary enclosure brought larger farms and also new roads which had the effect of making travel across the county much easier. Ruegg cited the journey of 14 miles from Piddlehinton to Lulworth which before enclosure would have involved the traveller in opening and shutting twenty-two gates, whereas now there were only five gates on the journey. The larger landowners had also provided greatly improved cottages for labourers, especially Henry Charles Sturt at Crichel and Tincleton, Lord Portman at Pimperne and Durweston, the Earl of Ilchester at Evershot and Abbotsbury, the Duke of Bedford at Swyre and Robert Williams at Bridehead. Labourers' Friendly Societies had also been established which provided some insurance against sickness and old age and prizes were awarded for allotment cultivation, garden produce, industrious service and economy, home duties and clean cottages, school attendance and needlework. Ruegg welcomed these improvements in the labourers' conditions but noted that 'They are indeed terribly addicted to beer, but intoxication is not very prevalent, though a mower will often drink two gallons of beer a day'. A 'crowning improvement' had occurred following an Act of Parliament of 1828 dealing with Cranborne Chase. This was the virtual extinction of the herds of some 12,000 deer which had previously ranged at large over the Chase, 'tending greatly to demoralise the habits of the labouring classes', and providing a major obstacle to any improvement in farming in fourteen parishes. Agriculture was now vastly improved; some 4,000 acres had been brought into cultivation; expensive deer fences were no longer needed, and even the productivity of the coppices which grew ash and hazel for sheep hurdles had been greatly improved. In particular Ruegg enthused over the amount of chalk downland which had been brought into cultivation.

> The extent to which the downs of Dorset have been broken up may, without exaggeration, be set at thousands of acres, and every year great quantities of such land are being converted into arable with infinite advantage alike to the landlord and the tenant.... The face of the whole district between Bryanstone and Milton Abbey has been changed, and the former furze brakes and heaths are become as fine a district as the county presents. Chesilborne - once a sheet of downs has been brought into excellent cultivation under Lord Rivers. Between Dorchester and Blandford there is scarcely a parish in which the downs have not been broken up.... In the neighbourhood of the chalk hills of Cerne the quantity of downland converted within the last ten years is put at 2,000 acres, and the land then worth 5s 0d is now become worth £2, and it is calculated that where one shepherd's boy was kept five men are now employed.

The third account of Dorset farming during the period of prosperity and 'high farming' of the mid-nineteenth century comes from two articles published in the *Journal* of the Bath and West of England Agricultural Society and written by a local farmer, Joseph Darby of Lytchett. His articles were published to coincide with two of the occasions when the Bath and West Show was held in Dorchester, one in 1861 and another in 1872. The first of Joseph Darby's articles dealt with 'Farming on the Chalk Soils of Dorset' (1861), and the second ranged more widely and dicussed 'The Farming of Dorset' (1872). In both articles Darby emphasised the enormous changes which had taken place in farming practice during the previous few decades. Like all other observers, he was particularly impressed by the enclosure and cultivation of the downlands, and wrote that

> the chalk hills formerly presented to view one vast sheet of downs; cultivation was confined to the valleys which intersected them, or to their slopes, where the land was of good natural fertility; but it seldom extended upwards to any distance from their bases, but what a change has been effected in their appearance!

Darby also described the dramatic change which this extension of arable and the planting of so many

Man and the Land
Farming in Dorset

The traditional Dorset landscape - Tyneham in 1927, with a three-horse binder, perfected in the 1870s and a much quicker way of harvesting grain than men with scythes. Gift of Ruth Saunders.

Left: The heathland at Affpuddle, the most difficult land in the county to farm. Much has been reclaimed or planted with conifers this century. Dorset County Museum Collection.

Below: Water meadows at Bradford Peverell in about 1900. A notable feature of the Dorset landscape producing early grass through flooding in winter. Sheep were pastured on them in spring, and cows usually in the autumn. Pouncey Collection.

Ploughing on the chalk at Piddletrenthide in 1940 or 1941. Much downland was brought into arable cultivation in the Second World War. Gift of Mr C. Langdon.

Dorchester sheep fair in 1962 (bottom) and the 1930s. Gift of J.M. Gill. Sheep were more important to Dorset farming in the past than they are now.

Right: Washing sheep near Arish Mell in the 1930s. Gift of Tessa Baumann.

Below: Sheep shearing at Mr Hooper's farm, Turnerspuddle in 1912. Gift of Mrs A. Hirst and Mrs G.L. Davis.

Left: Prize cow with brass horn tips, devices used to blunt and decorate the tips of the horns. About 1910. Gift of Mr and Mrs Butcher.

Below: Shorthorn bull at Vearse Farm, Symondsbury in the early 1920s, with the farmer George Randall. The shorthorn was the main dairy cow in Dorset in the mid and late 19th century. Gift of Muriel and Marjorie Randall.

Right: Milking in the yard at Horn Hill Dairy, Beaminster about 1911. The milkers are the farmer's sons. Gift of Mr and Mrs Butcher.

Below: In the barn at Heaves Farm, Piddletrenthide in 1940 or 1941. Miss Becky Mayo (the farmer's daughter) and a soldier milking. Gift of Mr C. Langton.

Left: Loading churns at Little Minterne Farm in 1952. Churns were used for moving milk from the 19th century up to the 1960s. Gift of Peter Lacey.

Below: Richard Shutler at West Lulworth Farm about 1910. The farm was mixed, with sheep and arable as well as the dairy herd of Shorthorns seen in the background. Gift of Peter Lacey

Right: Taking water from the river at Piddletrenthide for cattle pastured in the higher fields, about 1930. Gift of Mr K. Groves.

Below: Horses being watered at the river after work, at Uploders about 1910-1918. Gift of Muriel and Marjorie Randall.

Laying a hedge at Bloxworth in the 1930s. Percy House under instruction from his father, the farmer. Gift of Percy House.

Charles Mitchell with a two-wheeled cart, a putt, at New Buildings, Charminster in the 1930s, These small carts could be tipped up and were often used to take dung to the fields. Fine brick barn in the background. Gift of Nancy Puckett.

Right: Ploughing near Swanage in the later 19th century. The ploughman wears a smock. Pouncey Collection.

Below: Hoeing at Charminster about 1910. Gift of Sheila Gillard

Left: The four mowers - on one of the earliest photographs of Dorset labourers, taken at Piddletrenthide in 1863 or 1864. The four were a mowing team of Eli Saint (leader), Job Saint, Bob Hodges and Ned Trim. Gift of Mrs E.D. Thompson.

Below: Stooking oats at Admiston Farm, Puddletown in August 1952. The crop had been cut by tractor and binder, but still had to be stooked in the age-old way to dry. Gift of Diana Banfield.

Right: A rare photograph of women working on the land in the later 19th century. Probably threshing in the Sturminster Newton area. Gift of Roy Adam.

Below: Tractor pulling a binder which was built to be horse-drawn at Coombe Keynes in 1935. Gift of Mr E. Chutter.

Left: Mr G House (the farmer) of Bloxworth 'tucking' a hay rick - tidying it up after it had settled for 4-6 weeks and preparing it for thatching. Hay and corn ricks were a common sight until the 1950s. Gift of Mr Percy House.

Below: Taking home the corn harvest at Alton Pancras in the late 1940s, still using man and horse power. Gift of Joanna Havelock.

Steam transport for corn at Bovington during the First World War, using a requisitioned showman's engine. Gift of Peter Lacey.

Steam threshing at Manor Farm, Winterborne Steepleton in about 1927. Steam power transformed threshing from a task which lasted most of the winter to a few days' work. Gift of D.N.R. Coombe.

Captions by April Corner and Jo Draper
Published by the Dorset Natural History and Archaeological Society 1996 with the aid of a grant from the Mansel-Pleydel Trust.

Outside one of the barns at Upton Manor Farm, Uploders in about 1912. Edwin Randall (right) with labourers. Cider barrels and apples are ready in the cart for the cider making. Gift of Muriel and Marjorie Randall.

Horse gear at the Dairy Farm, Melplash about 1910. The horse walked round and round to supply power for machinery via the central gears. Gift of Mr and Mrs Butcher.

miles of new hedgerows had wrought on the landscape, and the destruction of so much archaeological evidence of former fields and settlements, 'the ancient landmarks are obliterated'. He also laid stress on the 'outstanding progress made in the agriculture of the cultivated districts during recent years', on the use of artificial fertilisers and of oil cake for consumption by sheep and cattle. The sheep flocks and associated water meadows remained a crucial element in chalkland farming. He gave numerous examples of progressive farmers in the county, of their crop rotations and of their large expenditure on labour, fertilisers and feedstuffs. Farms on the chalklands were very large, many over 1,000 acres, and for example, Mr J. Cains of Chesilborne whose 640 acres of arable included 400 acres of former downland which had been broken up during the previous decade, employed 54 men on his land and 'a very great outlay is necessitated by this high management'.

On the claylands of west Dorset and in the Blackmore vale, Darby described the new developments in butter and cheese making, the new market for fresh butter provided by the railways, and growth in the manufacture of Cheddar cheese 'or sufficiently good to pass off as Cheddar'. The dairy cows remained a mixture of crosses from Devon, Old Dorsets and Herefords, but Channel Island breeds and Shorthorns were gaining in popularity.

New farm buildings, especially on the farms belonging to some of the great estates, and greatly improved machinery including mowers, double-furrow ploughs, elevators for hay and straw, and new cultivators, harrows and iron rollers had brought great changes to farm work, while by 1872 ploughing and threshing using steam power 'has taken a good hold of the county'.

An indication of the new implements which were available and of local firms which had emerged as manufacturers or as agents for larger suppliers, can be obtained from the printed lists of exhibitors at the Bath and West shows. The 1872 show at Dorchester included exhibitions of steam ploughing, reapers, ploughs, drills, elevators, threshing machines, milk coolers and large-scale displays of seeds by Suttons

of Reading and Carters of London. There was even an early example of a milking machine invented by Richard Keevil of Trowbridge which had a small pump and 'small silver tubes which are inserted into the teats of the cow' and which delivered the milk into a pail. The annual five-day show was again held in Dorchester in 1887, and the long list of the firms who exhibited implements is naturally dominated by national firms such as Ransomes of Ipswich, Marshalls of Gainsborough, Fowlers of Leeds, Taskers of Andover, Burrells of Thetford, Clayton & Shuttleworth of Lincoln and Hornsby of Grantham. But local firms at the show included Reeves of Bratton (Wilts.); Dening and Co. of Chard; Brown and May of Devizes and John Wallis Titt of Warminster. Dorset firms included E.S. Hindley of Bourton; Pond and Son, Prize Dairy Works, Blandford; Robert B. Brown, Dorchester; Crocker and Co., The Iron Works, Dorchester; Sarah

Gwen Hole ready for milking at Elm Tree Farm, Holwell in 1919. Gift of Mrs P. Dimond.

Hazel, Engineer and Implement Maker, Dorchester; Gentry Company, Blandford and B. & G. Taylor, Louds Iron Works, Dorchester.

Although the changes on the chalklands during these 'golden years' of Victorian farming were the most dramatic and had such a profound effect on the landscape, nonetheless the claylands of north and west Dorset also shared in the prosperity of these years. Cheese and butter making, together with the rearing of pigs and veal calves flourished. Blue Vinney was made on many farms and Dorset fresh butter enjoyed a high reputation in the London market and commanded the best prices. Cows continued to be leased by farmers to dairymen at the rate of £8-£10 per cow per year. Returns averaged £14-£16 per cow depending on the management of the herd and the skill of the dairy-maids. These prosperous middle years of the nineteenth century are the period in which is set the picture of a south Dorset dairy farm in Hardy's *Tess of the D'Urbervilles*, where a happy community of dairy-men and dairy-maids were employed to manage and process the milk of a herd of 100 cows and where Dairyman Dick was sufficiently affluent to dress in shining broad-cloth on Sundays and be addressed as Mister Richard Crick. The process of farm cheese-making was revolutionised during the mid-nineteenth century by the work of Joseph Harding of Marksbury (Somerset). He introduced scientific methods into the dairy in the place of the old practice which depended upon the dairymaid's skill, insisting on absolute cleanliness and the use of the thermometer, hydrometer, and acetometer. He also designed improved equipment including a revolving curd breaker and double-sided tin vats which used a jacket of water to bring the milk to exactly the right temperature before the rennet was added. From the 1870s the availability of standardised rennet removed another source of difficulty from the process. Harding's methods were publicised through the *Journal* of the Bath and West Society, by lectures and through 'dairy schools', and the meticulous attention to detail which he recommended produced a Cheddar cheese with far less variation in quality and consistency. Most of the

Dorset dairy farms in the Blackmore Vale and in the clay vales of west Dorset remained small family-run enterprises, but on the arable farms of the chalk downlands the tendency for farm sizes to increase continued as estate owners and stewards amalgamated farms and encouraged the more successful tenants to take on greater acreages. As the Director of the Rothamsted Experimental Station, A.D. Hall, was to comment after a journey across Salisbury Plain and into Dorset in 1910, the chalk downs were no place for the small holder

When the depth of the soil can be measured in inches the farming must be based upon sheep, and no small farm can pay its way with sheep.

Farm Labourers

Although conditions slowly improved, the work of Dorset farm labourers remained hard and poorly paid. A remarkable description of his early years was written by William Saint who was born at Doles Ash Farm near Piddletrenthide in 1864 and lived there until the age of nineteen. His father worked as a labourer/carter/shepherd on the farm, and William was the third of six children. The farm was 1,200 acres and besides the farmer, Samuel Symes, and the bailiff, nine men were employed as well as numerous other men and women who were hired for specific jobs or at harvest time. He gives a vivid description of the low wages (8 shillings per week) and the poor housing conditions, the very long hours and the heavy labour involved in jobs such as ploughing, mowing, threshing with a flail, and furze cutting. William Saint left school at the age of seven, and began work on the farm for 1s 6d per week, at first tending the pigs and bird scaring, later becoming a plough-boy, then labourer at 5s 0d a week and finally a carter until he left at the age of nineteen to join the police force. One recollection of his childhood serves to illustrate the poverty in which many farm labourers' families lived

the farmer gave each family a joint of beef at Christmas, and we never tasted beef or mutton at any other time of the year. I know it is hard to believe this, but it is true.

The Great Estates

At the height of the period of prosperity brought about by all the innovations of 'high farming', a Parliamentary Report of 1874 revealed for the first time the true extent and wealth of the great estates which dominated Dorset. The enquiry into the ownership of land was made by order of Parliament in 1872-3 and the results were published in 1874, showing for the first time since the Domesday Survey of 1086 the precise figures regarding the landowners, the size of their estates and the size of their annual income. It showed that 36 per cent of Dorset was occupied by estates of more than 10,000 acres, whereas the national average was 24 per cent; while 35 per cent of Dorset was occupied by estates of between 1,000 and 10,000 acres against a national average of 29 per cent. The enquiry also showed that in Dorset ten peers owned between them 122,625 acres or some 20 per cent of the whole county, while a further 24 'great landowners' together owned 192,847 acres or 32 per cent of the total area. As will be seen from the accompanying table, some of these landowners also possessed very large acreages elsewhere, providing them with enormous incomes at a time when farm labourers on their Dorset estates were earning about 10s 0d per week with which to support their families. The first line of figures shows the acreage of land owned in Dorset together with its annual value; the second line shows all the land owned, including that in Dorset, and the total income from the whole estate.

MAJOR LANDOWNERS IN DORSET 1874

	Acres	Gross Annual Value
Lord Alington, More Crichel, Wimborne		
Dorset:	14,756	£21,140
Total:	17,500	£23,624
Walter Ralph Bankes, Kingston Lacy		
Dorset:	19,228	£14,985
Duke of Bedford, Woburn Abbey, Bedford [Kingston Russell]		
Dorset:	3,412	£3,996
Total:	86,335	£141,793 [+London property]
Rev. Nathaniel Bond, Creech Grange, Wareham		
Dorset:	7,429	£4,499
Total:	7,794	£5,614
W.E. Brymer, Ilsington House, Puddletown		
Dorset:	4,831	£5,152
William Montagu Calcraft, Rempstone Hall Wareham		
Dorset:	4,854	£4,503
Total:	7,429	£6,410
George Digby Wingfeld-Digby, Sherborne Castle		
Dorset:	21,230	£36,106
Total:	26,854	£46,092
John Samuel Wanley Sawbridge-Erle-Drax, Charborough Park		
Dorset:	15,069	£11,631
Total:	23,587	£23,165
Mrs Egginton, Bere Regis		
Dorset:	5,301	£4,766
Total:	8,007	£8,340
Earl of Eldon, Shirley House, Croydon [Encombe, Kingston]		
Dorset:	6,869	£8,192
Total:	25,761	£28,457
James John Farquharson, Langton House, Blandford		
Dorset:	6,063	£7,300
Henry Richard Farquharson, Eastbury House, Tarrant Gunville		
Dorset:	5,476	£3,680
Rev. William Charlton Frampton, Moreton House		
Dorset:	8,998	£6,047
Sir Richard George Glyn, Gaunts House, Wimborne		
Dorset:	9,770	£12,676
Rt. Hon. Lord Richard Grosvenor, Stalbridge Park		
Dorset:	4,762	£9,944
Baron Charles Joseph Theophilus Hambro, Milton Abbey		
Dorset:	9,622	£12,000
Earl of Ilchester, Redlynch, Bruton [Melbury House]		
Dorset:	15,981	£18,515
Total:	32,849	£43,452

John Clavell Mansel-Pleydell, Whatcombe
House, Blandford
Dorset: 8,699 £7,435
Viscount Portman, Bryanston
Dorset: 7,798 £9,478
Total: 33,891 £49,972
Major-Gen. Fox-Pitt-Rivers, Rushmore
Dorset: 24,942 £33,682
Total: 27,704 £35,396
Marquis of Salisbury, Hatfield House
[Cranborne]
Dorset: 3,118 £2,922
Total: 20,202 £33,413
Earl of Sandwich, Hooke Court
Dorset: 5,268 £5,693
Earl of Shaftesbury, Wimborne St Giles
Dorset: 17,317 £12,536
Total: 21,785 £16,083
Richard Brinsley Sheridan, Frampton Court
Dorset: 11,468 £12,765
Lord Stalbridge, Motcombe House
Dorset: 13,556 £31,409
Reginald Joseph Weld, Lulworth Castle
Dorset: 15,478 £13,704
Total : 15,525 £13,854
Marchioness of Westminster, Motcombe House
Dorset: 8,794 £21,265
Total: 12,906 £26,958
E. Williams, Herringston
Dorset: 7,349 £2,259
Robert Williams, Bridehead
Dorset: 4,917 £6,400
Total: 4,931 £7,000
Lord Wimborne, Canford Manor
Dorset: 17,400 £17,543
Total: 83,539 £46,856

It was the huge income enjoyed by some of the
leading landowners in Dorset that enabled them to
support a lavish lifestyle and maintain houses and
establishments of the size of Melbury House,
Canford Manor, Rushmore, Sherborne Castle,
Lulworth Castle and Wimborne St Giles. For the
landowners their estates not only provided a secure

source of wealth, but also established their social
position and political power in the county, and their
expenditure on all the 'trappings of wealth'
considered essential features of life in a great
mansion was huge. The Earl of Shaftesbury had an
indoor staff of 27 at St Giles House, as well as
coachmen, stable boys, gardeners, gamekeepers and
other outdoor servants. It was in order to obtain
social standing and political influence that Sir John
Guest, whose large fortune was based on iron
foundries in south Wales, purchased the Canford
estate with some 17,000 acres in 1845. The purchase
price of £354,000 brought him not only a fine house
and substantial landed property, but it also gave him
political influence in the parliamentary borough of
Poole and also represented a great advance in his
social position. The rise from industrial wealth to
landed aristocratic status was completed by Sir John
Guest's son who became Lord Wimborne. The most
ostentatious use of wealth and the most total
example of aristocratic power and assurance can be
seen in one of the last of the great country mansions
to be built. This was Lord Portman's huge new
mansion at Bryanston, built during the 1890s. Its
stark, uncompromising outline, emphasised by the
bright red of its brickwork, dominates the town of
Blandford Forum and the surrounding countryside.
Like several other Dorset landowners, Lord Portman
had the advantage of a huge income from his London
property, but for those landowners dependent upon
income from agricultural land the period of
prosperity, high rents and secure income had come
to an end by 1880.

The Agricultural Depression

A run of cold, wet summers and poor grain yields
after 1878 coincided with a sharp fall in the price of
both corn and cheese as imports flooded into
England from the United States, Canada, Australia,
New Zealand and elsewhere. The first shipments of
refrigerated meat from Australia reached England in
1880, and this was soon followed by beef from
Argentina, lamb, mutton, cheese and butter from
New Zealand, cheap grain from Canada and the
United States, and wool from Australia. The
unseasonable summers from 1878 to 1882 brought

cattle disease, liver rot in sheep and corn crops which barely repaid the cost of harvesting. Hardest hit were the farmers on the chalklands who were dependent upon the sale of corn for their livelihood. Wheat which in 1847 had sold for 70s 0d per quarter had already fallen to 46s 0d by 1870 and by 1894 was down to 24s 0d per quarter. As a result more and more land was laid down to grass, numerous farmers were unable to pay their rent and the income of estate owners fell dramatically. The author, Rider Haggard, who visited Dorset in 1901 to collect material for his survey of *Rural England*, wrote that 'From Yeovil to Dorchester ... it is pasture, pasture all the way, scarcely relieved by the sight of a single piece of arable'. Throughout Dorset the 1880s and 1890s saw a steady fall in the prices of corn, wool, meat and dairy products, numerous bankruptcies and dwindling rent rolls for the landowners.

In the face of competition from imported cheese many Dorset dairy farms abandoned cheese-making altogether concentrating on the supply of liquid milk, either by rail to London and other towns or to the newly-formed cheese factories producing standardised Cheddar cheese which rapidly supplanted farm-made cheeses such as Blue Vinney. Throughout the 1880s and 1890s it was the sale of liquid milk which kept many farmers in business who would otherwise have faced ruin from the fall in prices of corn and meat. Factory-produced butter became a practical possibility after the invention of the centrifugal separator which was first exhibited by the Royal Agricultural Society in 1879. At the same time the production of Cheddar cheese had been reduced to a standard process capable of accurate control and the virtual elimination of poor or variable quality. The Semley Dairy company was founded in 1871 and was later united with the Gillingham Dairy Company, while by 1882 the Surrey Farm Dairy Company had a depot at nearby Tisbury. During the 1880s the Semley milk depot was advertising a twice daily dispatch of cooled milk

'Receiving platform, Sturminster Newton & District Farmers Ltd'. A postcard postmarked 1914. The milk floats backed up to the platform had brought the milk to this 'factory'. Note the huge 17 gallon churns of milk up on the platform. Gift of D.T. Fox.

from 3,000 cows in Dorset for the London market. In 1891 a cheese factory was established at Lydlinch by Mr Wingfield Digby, and by 1895 it was receiving 1,200 gallons of milk each day and producing high-quality, prize-winning Cheddar cheese, as well as sending milk to London via Stalbridge. In 1904 the West Surrey Central Dairy Company established a milk factory at Beaminster producing dried milk products marketed as 'Cow and Gate'.

The statistics show the dramatic impact of the prolonged agricultural depression. Between 1875 and 1913 the acreage of permanent pasture in the county rose from 231,759 acres to 315,161 acres, with a corresponding decline in the acreage of arable from 524,297 in 1875 to 292,973 in 1913, and many hundreds of acres of water meadows went out of use

as the old sheep-corn husbandry was no longer maintained on the chalklands. The sheep flocks were badly hit by the fall in the price of wool in the face of competition from Australia and New Zealand, and also because of the decline in the traditional folding of the sheep on the arable as the cultivated acreage declined, as artificial manures became readily available and as the old equation of 'more sheep - more corn' became increasingly invalid. Sheep numbers in Dorset fell from about 500,000 in 1895 to 300,000 in 1900 and to 46,000 by 1947. Farm buildings and routine husbandry were neglected as low prices continued to bite into profits, more and more land was laid down to poor-quality grass, water meadows fell into disuse, cottages were untenanted, markets and fairs and even the traditional market dinners, 'the market ordinaries' declined or ceased. The cultivation of flax in the

Cheese-makers at the East Stour School for teaching dairy work about 1918. Formal agricultural training is a 20th century phenomenon. Gift of John and Lorna Perrin.

county virtually disappeared in the face of foreign competition, and whereas in 1838 there were 18 flax mills in Dorset, by 1873 foreign competition had reduced the acreage to 712 and by 1881 it had fallen to 225; in 1894 the acreage grown had shrunk to a mere 25 acres and by 1900 the cultivation of flax in the county had ceased altogether. Only the production and sale of liquid milk remained secure from foreign competition, and this is reflected in the increase in number of cattle kept in Dorset from 77,372 in 1875 to 93,947 by 1913, while at the same time the number of pigs kept rose from 42,000 to 46,000. The agricultural depression also led to a sharp decline in the population of most Dorset villages as can be seen from examples cited on page 11. The change from arable to pasture farming together with the widespread contraction of agricultural activity during the long years of the depression meant that the demand for labour was greatly reduced, and between 1871 and 1911 the number of labourers employed on Dorset farms fell by 31 per cent, and about one-fifth of all Dorset farmers gave up their farms between 1875 and 1902. The mid-Victorian period of high rents and secure income for the great landowners also came to an end with the depression. Between 1872 and 1892 the average rent of farm land in Dorset fell by 13.4 per cent, and even so it became increasingly difficult to find suitable tenants for farms; the period 1892 to 1911 saw an even sharper decline and average rents fell by a further 16.8 per cent.

In the absence of any tariff barriers, there was no way in which British farmers could compete with the flood of cheap grain arriving from the U.S.A. and Canada, with low-priced beef from Argentina, or with mutton, lamb, butter and cheese arriving in refrigerated ships from Australia and New Zealand. So serious was the situation that a Royal Commission was appointed in 1894 to enquire into the Agricultural Depression. Henry Rew, one of the assistant commissioners, visited Dorset in 1895 and his informative report paints an extremely depressing picture of the agricultural situation he found in the county. He attended a meeting of farmers at Bere Regis where a resolution was passed stating that 'The farming of arable land has become absolutely unprofitable on account of the low price of produce'. The figures which were given for the average prices at Blandford market tell their own story (see table below).

Henry Rew gave many details of the consequences of these low prices. Rents were falling sharply, it was becoming more and more difficult for landowners to find tenants willing to take farms on their estates, the acreage of arable land had contracted sharply and throughout the chalklands land was being abandoned to scrub and rabbits. He observed that 'The ownership of land is rapidly becoming a luxury which only men possessing other sources of income can enjoy'. After talking to numerous farmers and landowners throughout the county, Rew stated that

Some of the best and most substantial - and in times past the most successful - farmers in the South of England were to be found in Dorset, but with the present outlook it appears that the race is likely to die out.... Many hang on, but cannot obtain a fair return on their capital.... Capital is surely and steadily leaving the land.

	1847	1862	1872	1880	1888	1893
Wheat per qtr.	70s 0d	55s 5d	57s 0d	40s 2d	32s 10d	26s 7d
Barley per qtr.	40s 0d	35s 1d	37s 3d	31s 2d	29s 0d	26s 0d
Oats per qtr.		22s 7d	23s 2d	20s 0d	16s 7d	18s 3d
Fat Sheep			60s 0d		30s 0d	
Lambs			42s 0d		20s 0d	
Wool per lb.				1s 4d		0s 11½d

Average prices at Blandford Market 1847-1893

His pessimistic conclusion was that

> ... it is impossible to view the situation in Dorset as a whole without gloomy forebodings of the immediate future of agriculture.

Only the market for liquid milk for supplying London and the growing resorts of Weymouth and Bournemouth offered a gleam of light in an otherwise dark picture.

Farming before the First World War

The account of Dorset farming written by H. Rider Haggard, better known as the author of *King*

Tory's Barton, Turnworth, in the 1890s. The half barrels are for cattle food. The granary background right is on steddle stones to keep out the rats. Pouncey Collection, Dorset County Museum.

Solomon's Mines, was part of description of rural conditions made following an extended journey throughout England in 1901 and 1902, and published in two volumes as *Rural England* in 1903. This provides a good picture of the effect which the previous twenty years of severe depression had produced in the county. The journeys were sponsored by the *Daily Express* and the summary accounts of farming in each county first appeared as articles in the newspaper. Everywhere he went Rider Haggard encountered deep gloom and anxiety among the farming communities who were finding it increasingly difficult to make a living from the land in the face of unrelenting foreign competition. As one Cornish farmer put it

> The English farmer might perhaps compete with any one foreign country, but under our system of Free Trade he must compete with the whole world.

Rider Haggard travelled through the central part of Dorset from Yetminster to Dorchester and thence to Milton Abbas, Bulbarrow Hill, Turnworth, Bryanston and Blandford Forum. In addition he corresponded with several landowners, land agents, farmers and others in the county including Thomas Hardy, and obtained their views on farming, labourers, rents, prices, cottages and rural conditions. Based on this evidence his conclusion was that

> ...it is impossible to take a favourable view of the present prospects of the land, or of any class connected with it, in Dorsetshire.

He was impressed by the character and ability of some of the farmers he met in Dorset, particularly by the Tory family who together farmed more than 6,000 acres in Winterborne Clenston, Turnworth and neighbouring parishes. The Torys were long-established and careful farmers, proud of their fine crops of barley and of their well-known flock of Dorset Down sheep. But they, like other farmers, told a sorry tale of low prices, and of landowners who could not get an economic rent for their land so that only those with other sources of income could survive. Above all, they lamented the depopulation of villages, the flight of working people to better-paid jobs in the towns, and the difficulty of getting skilled labour for farm work. One of Rider Haggard's correspondents, the Rev. Octavius Pickard-Cambridge, who had been rector of Bloxworth since 1868, laid the blame for rural depopulation squarely at the door of education, and

> was strongly of opinion that the keeping of boys at school until they are thirteen, tends very much to decrease the number of agricultural hands. No lad who did not begin farm work long before that age would embrace it unless he was obliged, and even if he began then he would escape from it as soon as he could, while if he stayed upon the land he never became so useful or efficient a labourer as those of the old times, when lads were always put to the business at eight or nine years old.

Others, more realistically, spoke of the low wages, long hours, the dullness of village life compared to the towns, and the poor condition of many of the farm cottages. 'How could a girl who had been in service be expected to live in a hovel when she married?'. Even on Lord Portman's Bryanston estate, where the agent, James Forrester, showed Rider Haggard how 'everything is managed without thought of cost', and where he was greatly impressed by the fine farm buildings illuminated with electric light produced by a generator which 'reminds the visitor of the engines of some great ship', as well as by the fine herds of North Devon and Guernsey cattle, and where the cottages were well-built and comfortable, the labourers could not be persuaded to stay. ' "They won't be kept", said Mr Forrester, "But male and female, depart, mostly to take service in shops" '. The steward of another neighbouring, unnamed estate, provided figures illustrating the dire state of agriculture in the Blandford Forum district.

Farm A

In 1852 it let for £1 per acre

In 1880 it let for 31s 8d per acre

In 1901 it let for 12s 6d per acre

Farm B

(549 acres of which one third is pasture)

In 1862 it let for £650

In 1901 it let for £250 tithe-free

Farm C

(396 acres)

In 1852 it let for £300

In 1862 it let for £450

In 1901 it let for £240

Farm D

Grassland - 180 acres

In 1852 it let for £235, plus £46 tithe paid by tenant

In 1878 it let for £352, plus £46 tithe paid by tenant

In 1901 it let for £262, minus tithe, paid by landlord.

The one bright spot in the otherwise depressing account of the condition of Dorset farming given by Rider Haggard was the story of the Rew Farm small-holdings at Martinstown. The Rew Manor farm had been purchased by Sir Robert Edgcumbe of Sandy in Bedfordshire with the intention of creating a number of small-holdings on the land. It consisted of 343 acres which were purchased for £5,050. The farmhouse and a water meadow were then sold, leaving 307 acres which were divided into 80 lots varying in size from 1 to 9 acres. All were sold at prices ranging from £7 to £20 per acre, one-tenth of the purchase money to be paid at once and the rest spread over nine years. Twenty-seven purchasers took up the offer of the holdings, some buying several small plots, and within six years almost all had paid off the purchase price; they included farm labourers, gardeners, coachmen, stone-masons, a postman, policeman, blacksmith, shopkeeper and two watchmakers. The scheme proved to be a great success. Cottages, farm buildings and greenhouses were built by the new owners, and the production from the land was greatly increased, Sir Robert Edgcumbe recouped

his initial outlay, and the population supported by the land rose from the 21 people living on Rew Manor farm to 100 small-holders and their families.

The First World War and Its Aftermath

The twentieth century has witnessed a vast increase in the machinery employed on farms and a corresponding decrease in the demand for labour and for horses. By the outbreak of the first World War in 1914 the increasing use of steam power, stationary oil engines, modern fencing particularly barbed wire, new artificial manures and food-stuffs and a greatly increased range of mass-produced implements was altering the pace and character of farming, and diminishing the demand for skilled specialist labour. Stationary oil engines such as those manufactured by R.A. Lister and Co. of Dursley (Glos) or by Petters of Yeovil began to appear on farms from the early twentieth century, many of them replacing the more expensive and inconvenient steam engines for working barn machinery including the root cutters, chaff cutters and oil-cake breakers which became increasingly common. During the First World War tractors appeared on some of the larger farms, most of the early makes being imported from America such as the Titan, Mogul, Overtime and Moline. These were expensive and not always reliable, and it was not until after the war that British makes and in particular the Fordson became a common sight and began the slow process of replacing horses as the major motive power on farms. After the War, tractors, reaper-binders and milking machines began slowly to bring about major changes in working practices, but early machinery was often unreliable, depreciated quickly and gained only slow acceptance, while until relatively cheap and efficient tractors such as the Case and the Fordson became readily available during the 1930s many farmers remained committed to their horses. One major change on many dairy farms came with the introduction of the Hosier bail milking system, an easily transportable milking parlour which was used in the fields, and which meant that lands remote from farmsteads and on the chalk downlands could, in conjunction with a piped water supply, support herds of dairy cows, and the purpose-built machine milking system (the bail) could be moved all over the available pasture. The system was invented by A.J. Hosier of Wexcombe near Collingbourne Ducis in Wiltshire where a factory was established to manufacture the prefabricated milking bails which rapidly became popular all over the west country. The concentration upon the production of liquid milk for the London market or for the newly-created Cheddar cheese factories meant that arable farming in Dorset continued to decline, only recovering to its former levels during the Second World War. In 1875 some 38 per cent of Dorset land was cultivated; by 1929 this had shrunk to 15½ per cent, and in 1938 only 11.2 per cent was arable. In contrast the acreage devoted to cattle feed such as kale, mangolds and other fodder crops, and to grassland for hay and the increasingly popular silage continued to expand.

The interruption in the supply of imported foodstuffs during the First World War brought a temporary period of renewed prosperity to Dorset farms. Farming was controlled and directed as never before, with a Board of Agriculture, Ministry of Food, War Agricultural Executive Committees, guaranteed prices for cereals, meat, milk and potatoes, and fixed minimum wages for labourers. Food production campaigns led to a considerable increase in arable acreage as grassland was once more ploughed up for wheat, barley, oats and potatoes. These activities were enforced and supervised by the War Agricultural Executive Committee, and labour was provided by the Womens' Land Army, prisoners of war, the army and volunteers. With the ending of the war in 1918, however, the pressure and enforcement of cultivation orders were gradually abandoned, guaranteed prices came to an end, and farmers had once more to face foreign competition. By the mid 1920s Danish bacon, New Zealand butter and lamb, Canadian cheese and Argentinian beef were once again supplying more than half of the British market, and many Dorset farmers were only saved from ruin by the still buoyant market for liquid milk, although even here prices were greatly reduced under pressure from the large wholesalers such as United Dairies and Express Dairies who dominated the trade.

There were however some more hopeful signs, although much experimentation and new ideas for improvements in farming practice were financed by men whose secure fortunes had been made in industry or commerce. One example was J.H. Ismay, whose wealth derived from the White Star Shipping Line of Liverpool. In 1902 at the age of 35 he retired from business and purchased the Iwerne Minster estate of over 3,000 acres, where he remained until his death in 1930. At Iwerne Minster which had previously belonged to the wealthy banker and politician, Lord Wolverton, who had built the large Clayesmore House, Ismay introduced the most modern agricultural techniques, with new farm buildings, farm houses and eighty cottages, and even a village club for the social well-being of the community. As his obituary in *The Times* expressed it, 'No village was ever more fortunate in its owner'. His farming innovations included the introduction and trials of new varieties and strains of arable crops and grasses in which he cooperated with the Rothamsted Experimental Station. He concentrated a good deal of his efforts on his livestock, introducing a noted herd of Dairy Shorthorns, herds of Berkshire and Middle White pigs and a flock of Hampshire Down sheep. He also established a poultry farm and a bacon factory. The whole farming enterprise, while clearly supported by a fortune derived from other sources, nonetheless provided for other Dorset farmers an example of the most modern techniques and best farming practice. Likewise in 1914 Sir Ernest Debenham used the wealth generated by his London drapery business to purchase an estate at Briantspuddle with other property at Affpuddle, Tolpuddle, Turnerspuddle, Shitterton and Milborne St Andrew, and began to create a model estate using the most up-to-date and scientific methods. Debenham called his estate Bladen Farms, and he provided new farm buildings, farm houses and cottages, built in an attractive, traditional style, with piped water and electric power. High-quality pedigree livestock, sheep, cattle and pigs, were introduced, and associated businesses included a milk factory (first at Briantspuddle and later in large buildings at Milborne St Andrew), milling, egg production, forestry, together with the latest methods of arable and livestock farming. The Bladen farms comprised 3,000 acres, including 1,000 acres of arable which was worked by Fordson tractors and grew wheat, oats, swedes, kale, vetch and Italian rye grass. Four hundred acres of water meadow were restored and brought back into use. The herd of 500 tuberculin-tested cows comprised 50 pedigree Guernseys and 450 Dairy Shorthorns which were milked three times a day at 5 am, 1 pm and 7 pm, in a well-built modern milking parlour. Their feed was supplemented by concentrates provided by Dairy Nuts containing maize, rice, linseed, coconut, palm kernel and molasses. The dairy at Milborne St Andrew was equipped to deal with 10,000 gallons of milk each day or more if required, and other establishments dealt with the manufacture of butter and cheese and the disposal of whey. The herd of 900 pigs included separate flocks of Berkshire, Large White and Tamworth and these were also fed on carefully-balanced concentrates. Two flocks of pedigree Dorset Down sheep were kept and one

flock of Hampshire. As at Iwerne Minster the model farming was accompanied by concern for community life, and as well as providing work for people in the surrounding villages, and attempting to reverse the drift of farm workers away from the land, Sir Ernest Debenham built attractive new cottages at Briantspuddle and converted an old barn into a village hall and meeting place. Most of the building materials used on the farms and for the new cottages were manufactured or derived from the estate itself, the designs were created in the estate office and the enterprises also included a brick-works, lime kiln and saw mill. Sir Ernest Debenham was created a baronet in 1931 for 'services to Agriculture'; he died in 1952 and after his death the estate was sold and the farms were broken up. The whole project was intended as an example for neighbouring farms and for the whole country of the way in which employment could be provided in a rural area and of how home-grown food production could be dramatically and profitably increased. Visitors were encouraged and

A demonstration of Debenham's patented hay sweep and tractor-driven baler at Tonerspuddle Farm in the 1920s. Sir Ernest Debenham is among the group on the left. Gift of Briantspuddle Hall Committee.

the objectives of Sir Ernest Debenham's farming enterprises were clearly set out in the brochures he had printed giving details of the farming projects. In 1929 he wrote

> The Bladen Farms should be considered as an experiment initiated with the chief object of ascertaining whether, under modern conditions, and with the resources and facilities supplied to agriculture by recent scientific discoveries, it is possible for Dorset (and inferentially for Great Britain as a whole) to produce a larger proportion of home-grown foods, especially of animal origin, than it does at present. That it should do so would probably be generally admitted to be desirable, since it would readjust the balance of population and enable a larger number of workers to live on the land.

Another remarkable agricultural experiment was begun at Fontmell Magna in 1927 when the idealist and convert to the ideas of self-sufficiency and organic farming, Rolf Gardiner, inherited the 1,500 acre Springhead estate. Here he began 'work-camps' to reclaim derelict land and to plant timber on the steep downland slopes, while reorganising the farming practices on his estate and establishing local industries, mills, milk factories, saw-mills, etc., to process the produce of his land. His projects included re-planting woodland on Cranborne Chase, the establishment of a large flock of Dorset Down sheep, a herd of milking cows and a pig farm, the introduction of ideas of organic farming, self-sufficiency and small-holdings. He also re-introduced flax-growing to Dorset and set up a flax mill at Slape near Netherbury. He organised music, drama, and poetry festivals for the groups of young volunteers who came to work on his land, and led them on long walks along the downland trackways. These activities attracted considerable public interest and during the later 1930s some disapproval because of the involvement of German youth groups.

More important to most Dorset farmers during the years of depression in the 1920s and 1930s was the continuing demand for liquid milk and the

official encouragement of dairy farming to supply the increasing population of the towns. The figures for cattle and dairy cows tell their own story of the increasing dominance of the dairy industry in Dorset farming. In 1875 there were 55,000 cattle in the county, of which 45,000 were dairy cows; by 1929 the figures had risen to 104,000 cattle, of which some 52,000 were dairy cows. By 1949 numbers had increased to 150,000 cattle of which 66,000 were dairy cows, and even the traditional corn-growing areas of the chalklands had turned increasingly to dairy farming and away from the centuries-old reliance on 'sheep and corn' husbandry. National encouragement for dairy farmers included the important step of setting up the Milk Marketing Board in 1933 with tighter controls over quality and hygiene, careful milk recording, and a guaranteed

Stooking at Andover Green, Bovington Farm in 1935. Gift of Mr E. Chutter.

price structure. In 1934 a fat cattle subsidy was introduced for home-bred fat cattle with additional payments for quality stock. Encouragement was also given to the improvement of dairy herds, most notably through the provision of artificial insemination, and also through Attested and Accredited Herd schemes and through Tuberculin Tested licences. One result of these schemes, together with the effect of better winter housing for herds, improved feeding, piped water supplies to the fields, greater attention to breeding, management and veterinary care, was the greatly increased milk yield per cow. 'The thousand gallon per lactation', cow ceased to be a rarity and in some particularly well-managed herds much higher and even double such yields were obtained during the 1930s.

Like all other aspects of English life, Dorset farming was greatly affected by the years of acute economic depression during the 1930s, as industrial decline brought mass unemployment and sharply reduced the prices of home-grown produce, while increasing quantities of cheaper foreign foodstuffs of all kinds flooded the markets. The Ministry of Agriculture and Fisheries had been set up in 1920, and successive governments tried unsuccessfully to grapple with the problems of falling prices, cheap imports and over-production. In consequence farmers reverted to cost-cutting measures such as reduction in wages, allowing marginal land to go out of use, a retreat from arable farming and concentration upon milk, poultry, eggs and pigs. For some the growth of the holiday industry and the supply of produce to the growing suburbs around the resorts of Bournemouth, Christchurch, Poole, Swanage, Weymouth and Lyme Regis provided an essential lifeline in these difficult times. Even so the fixed costs of rent, interest, rates and tithe remained as an intolerable burden upon many farmers and there were numerous bankruptcies. Some help came in the form of subsidies or marketing boards during the 1930s. The Wheat Act of 1932 provided a standard price and deficiency payments for home-grown wheat, and in 1934 a subsidy was instituted for fat cattle to off-set the exceptionally low prices of the period, but sheep farmers received no help. Marketing Boards for Milk, potatoes and pigs also provided some assistance to farmers, and

Harry Davies, carter, having his lunch break, which he called 'namit', about 1930 at Cerne Abbas. Gift of Nancy Pucket.

the establishment of the Milk Marketing Board in 1933 was especially important for Dorset farmers, fixing prices and acting as a third party in all contracts for the sale of milk to wholesalers and retailers.

The Board also regulated quality and cleanliness, giving bonuses for milk from herds certified free of tuberculosis, and instituting a scheme to provide free milk in one-third of a pint bottles for needy schoolchildren, a project later extended to all children.

The conditions of the 1930s provided little incentive for Dorset farmers to invest in new equipment or machinery. Tractors were often unreliable and subject to rapid depreciation, while before the invention of the heavily-treaded tyre in the mid 1930s they could only provide satisfactory power on wet land by using metal wheels with strakes or luggs and these were forbidden on public roads. Moreover it was not always easy to adapt horse-drawn machinery to use with a tractor, and many farmers preferred to keep their horses rather than spend £140, which was the price of a new Fordson with straked wheels in 1935; pneumatic tyres added another £40 to the price.

Milking machines were also expensive, needed an oil-engine for power and could not always be used in older milking sheds. Moreover the rubber cups and tubes perished quickly from the constant sterilization and it was difficult to maintain the required vacuum. Only on the larger farms and with

Percy House with two horses which worked Marsh Farm, Bloxworth, about 1934. He worked for his father, the farmer. Gift of Percy House.

the larger dairy herds did either tractors or milking machines make much progress in Dorset until after the outbreak of the Second World War in 1939.

The Second World War

The war revolutionised farming in the county; home-produced foodstuffs became a major national priority, and numerous government directions and incentives were introduced to encourage farmers to increase production as an essential component of the war effort. War Agricultural Committees were set up with powers to compel farmers to make radical changes on their farms. Marketing Boards controlled sales and guaranteed prices. Subsidies, quotas, incentive schemes, acreage payments and assistance with mechanisation were all designed to ensure that domestic food production was increased to the maximum, and replaced the imports now made increasingly scarce by war conditions and the German submarine attacks on merchant shipping. The result of all the changes brought about during the early months of the war was dramatic. Labour on the farms was profoundly altered by the Women's Land Army, (the so-called 'Land-Girls',) and later by the employment of prisoners of war, Italian and German. Replacement of horses by tractors was vastly accelerated, so that by the end of the war the number of tractors had increased fourfold and they were the main source of motive power on most farms. New implements specifically designed for tractors were introduced, as were also combine harvesters, grain driers, milking machines, electric fencing and new techniques of silage making, cattle-feeding, hay-making and straw baling. The arable acreage was vastly increased both for corn production and for potatoes and vegetables and for cattle feed to replace imported products. In 1940, for example, there were 259 milking machines on Dorset farms; by 1949 there were 1,360.

Under pressure from local War Agricultural Executive committees, thousands of acres of land in the county were ploughed once more. Farmers could be and were fined for not ploughing for arable crops as instructed by local officials. As a result corn production was greatly increased while the potato acreage was multiplied fivefold as part of the national crusade to produce more food for the war effort. Grants were provided for ploughing up land that had been under grass for at least seven years, and county advisors and specialists were available to help with problems of pest infestation and to advise those who had long since abandoned arable husbandry. Flax-growing was encouraged in west Dorset, and by 1941 500 acres of flax were being grown to supply the Fontmell Industries mill at Netherbury which had formerly relied on imported supplies. As well as being used for a variety of fabrics, the flax was urgently required for the manufacture of fire-fighting hoses.

The national demand for home-grown food during the war and in the difficult years which followed meant that the decade from 1939 to 1949 saw more rapid and far-reaching changes in Dorset farming than ever before. Not all of these changes were to be permanent. Most of the female labour force was dispersed after the war and the arable acreage contracted from a high point of some 50% of the farmed area which was reached during the war. Many of the rigid controls upon farmers were relaxed, around many towns and villages farm land was taken for housing, shops and factories, while home-produced food was again compelled to compete with a growing stream of foreign imports. But many other war-time changes remained and many of the trends which were then introduced have continued. In particular, mechanisation has almost entirely replaced horses; combine harvesters, milking machines and the use of electricity have become almost universal, farm sizes have continued to increase, especially on the chalklands. The proliferation of subsidies, quotas and government incentives have remained a major force in determining the character of farming in the county. The application of scientific methods in plant breeding, cultivation, fertilisers, pesticides, fungicides and crop production, as well as in livestock breeding, management and veterinary care has continued to increase dramatically. The result is that any general survey of Dorset farming during the past 150 years must conclude that however remarkable the changes of the past have been, the real 'agricultural revolution' has occurred in the years since the beginning of the Second World War in 1939.

By the end of the war the number of horses employed in agriculture had fallen from nearly 14,000 in the 1930s to no more than 5,000; while the number of tractors on Dorset farms had grown to some 4,000 by 1945. Combine harvesters, grain driers, electricity, piped water supplies, highly mechanised milking parlours, artificial insemination and other modern innovations were increasingly being introduced on the larger farms. Meanwhile the vast sheep flocks for which Dorset was once so famous had declined until by 1947 there

were only some 47,000 sheep in the whole county. The combination of high labour costs and the availability of alternative sources of early feedstuffs likewise meant that by 1945 most of the water meadows, which had formerly played such a crucial part in chalkland husbandry, had ceased to be used.

The Post-War Period

Following the end of the war in 1945 the dairy industry resumed its predominance in Dorset farming, although large-scale cereal production continued on the increasingly extensive farms of the chalkland area.

A farm survey conducted by the University of Bristol in 1958 found that there were 3,029 farms in

A farm sale conducted by A.B. Duke in Purbeck in the late 1940s. A farm cart made a good rostrum. Gift of Oliver Duke.

the county of which 2,358 or 78 per cent were predominantly small dairy farms. As would be expected, these were mostly situated in north and west Dorset, and many were family-run farms of less than 150 acres. Approximately 66 per cent had herds of less than 30 cows; the largest herds being in the Blackmore Vale or the chalkland valleys while most of the smaller farms with fewer cows were situated in west Dorset. 215 farms or 7 per cent of the total concentrated on the raising of cattle and sheep, while 290 or 9.5 per cent were farms of less than 5 acres devoted to pigs, poultry or market gardening. The remaining 166 farms or 5.5 per cent of the total were mostly engaged in large-scale cereal production and were much larger than the rest, many being over

1,000 acres in extent. Even these figures for the large farms do not reveal the complete picture, since many cereal-producing farms were amalgamated to form much larger working units, employing the latest agricultural techniques and with huge capital investment in the latest machinery. The tendency for farm sizes to increase through amalgamations has continued, and by 1969 nearly 20 per cent of farms were over 1,000 acres.

The 'Agricultural Revolution'

Historians argue fiercely over when the agricultural revolution occurred, but for Dorset there is no doubt that it has happened during the last 150 years. A

Ploughing the chalk-re-seeding at Haydon Hill, Charminster in about 1956. The downs, originally all short turf supporting sheep, have been ploughed up since the 1860s. In the 19th century they were ploughed to be converted to arable: in the 20th century some (like that shown here) were resown with grass. Gift of Olive Miles.

farmer from any part of Dorset in 1850 would find today that almost every aspect of farming life has been transformed, and that the former characteristic features of farming in the county have disappeared. The old constants of soils and weather, seed-time and harvest of course remain, but all else has changed. On the chalklands the great flocks of folding sheep have vanished, the vast expanses of the downland have been enclosed by hedges and converted into arable, the water meadows are disused, and previously undreamt of yields of wheat and barley are obtained by the massive use of artificial fertilisers, pesticides, weed killers and fungicides. Working horses have vanished from the land, while tractors and ever-more complex machines enable these huge crops to be produced with far less manual toil and by a tiny proportion of the labour force which was once employed. Very few people work on the land, but a very large proportion of the population are interested and concerned at what happens to it. Conservation and ecology are important, and organic farming is increasing.

The size of farms, the capital investment required, the mechanisation, marketing and methods would all be totally bewildering to a Victorian farmer.

On the heath large acreages of acid soils have been reclaimed, drained and brought into cultivation and the land is farmed more intensively than would ever have been thought possible. Forestry, military activity, the holiday industry and even nuclear power have all changed the landscape beyond recognition. In the clay vales of the north and west of the county, the coming of the railways and later of refrigeration have created an entirely new demand for liquid milk from distant markets, while the milking machine has enabled the milk to be produced with far less labour. The old and diverse breeds of milking cows have given way to the almost universal Friesian with milk yields which would previously have been unbelievable, and the introduction of silage and manufactured feedstuffs has revolutionised their diet. A returning Victorian farmer would marvel to see the progress which has

been made in the application of scientific methods, biological research and mechanisation to all branches of agriculture. It would probably be foolhardy to risk the wrath of a Victorian farmer by any attempt to explain the absurdities of the Common Agricultural Policy, the creation of 'set-aside' land, the restriction of production by 'milk quotas', or the numerous attempts to find alternative uses for productive farmland. The Victorian farmer would be bewildered to see the widespread cultivation of crops such as maize, oil-seed rape and linseed, mechanised silage-making, modern dairy techniques and the modern specialisations such as all-arable farms, huge free-range pig units, and intensive calf, pig, poultry and egg production. Likewise he would be amazed at the extension of the control over prices and quality formerly exercised by the wholesale dairies to a wider range of products by the buying power of the major supermarkets. Perhaps above all he would be incredulous at the tiny proportion of the total population now directly engaged in agriculture. The total incomprehension which the Victorian farmer would experience in viewing all these changes is a measure of the revolution which has occurred in Dorset farming during the last 150 years.

Reading List

J.H. Bettey, *Rural Life in Wessex 1500-1900*, 1977.

J.H. Bettey, *Wessex from AD1000*, 1986.

J. Brown, *Farm Machinery 1750-1945*, 1989.

J. Caird, *English Agriculture in 1850-51*, 1852

John Fowles and Jo Draper, *Thomas Hardy's England* , 1984

A.D. Hall, *Pilgimage of British Farming*, 1913.

T. Hearing, *The Dorset Horn*, n.d. [1990]

B.A. Holdeness, *British Agriculture since 1945*, 1985.

B. Kerr, *Bound to the Soil: A Social History of Dorset 1750-1918*, 1968.

A.W.M. Roberts, *Farming in Dorset*, 1980.

L.H. Ruegg, 'Farming of Dorsetshire', *Journal of the Royal Agricultural Society of England*, 15(ii), 389-454.

L.E. Tavener, 'Dorset Farming 1900-1950', *Dorset Natural History and Archaeological Society Proceedings*, 75, 1953, 91-114.

E.H. Whetham, ed., *The Agrarian History of England and Wales, 1914-39*, 1978.

E.H. Whetham & C.S. Orwin, *History of British Agriculture 1846-1914*, 1963.

Much more information is also to be found in the printed *Parliamentary Papers & Royal Commission Reports* and in the *Journal of the Bath & West of England Society.*

Acknowledgments

The assistance of the following in the writing of this account is gratefully acknowledged:

Jo Draper, April Corner, Anthony Gannon, Jude James, Merry Ross.

Carters at Charminster early this century. Mr Charlie Foot (left) was head carter. Gift of Mr B. Foot.